BOUND & Gagged ™

BY DANA SUMMERS

TRIBUNE PUBLISHING

ORLANDO/1992

Cover design by Dana Summers and Bill Henderson

A publication of Tribune Publishing
and Tribune Media Services, Inc.

For information:
Tribune Publishing
P.O. Box 1100
Orlando, Florida 32801

Tribune Publishing

Editorial Director: George C. Biggers III
Managing Editor: Dixie Kasper
Senior Editor: Kathleen M. Kiely
Production Editor: Ken Paskman
Editorial Designer: Bill Henderson

Printed in the United States

First edition: November 1992

ISBN 0-941263-63-0

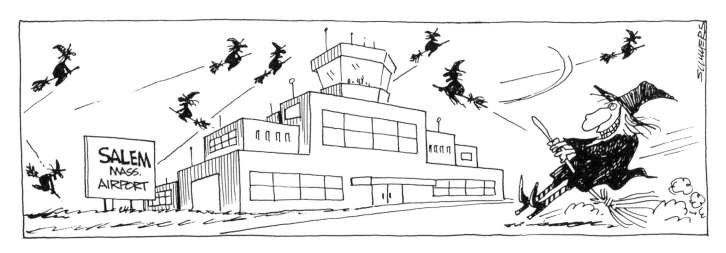

MORON
BANK
ROBBERS

BANK

Sell your books at
sellbackyourBook.com!
Go to sellbackyourBook.com
and get an instant price
quote. We even pay the
shipping - see what your old
books are worth today!

Inspected By: martha_diaz

00038543540

3540

0003854

$540

$540

0038283040

HERBAL MEDICINE WALK-IN CLINIC

PRESCRIPTION
Rx

AL'S GARDENING CENTER

WORLD'S GREATEST STUNTMAN'S FUNERAL

BLAM!

SUMMERS

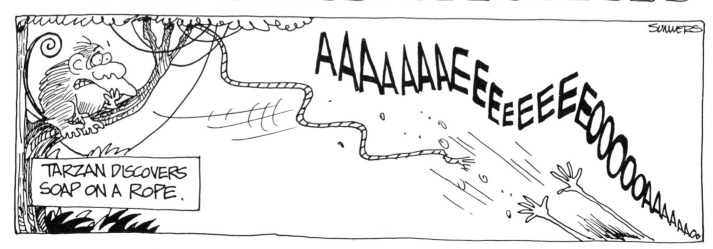

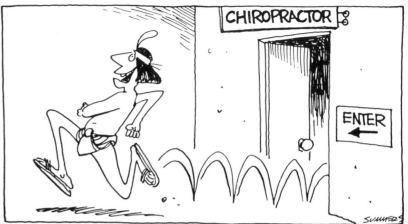

CRASH!

The National Squealer
WEEKLY TABLOID

PARKING · PUBLISHER · · EDITOR · · MANAGING EDITOR · · ELVIS ·

SUMMERS

METRO GENETIC LABS, INC.

BEWARE OF THE DOG

Summers

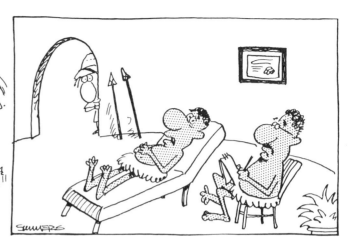

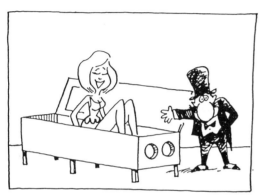

ARSON IN
ALASKA

BIKERS AND
THEIR
OLD LADIES

SOLITARY
CONFINEMENT

CHAIR LIFT

DELUXE CHAIR LIFT

LA-Z BOY

LA-Z BOY

Summers

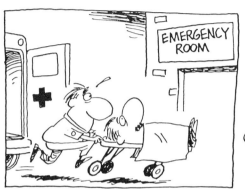

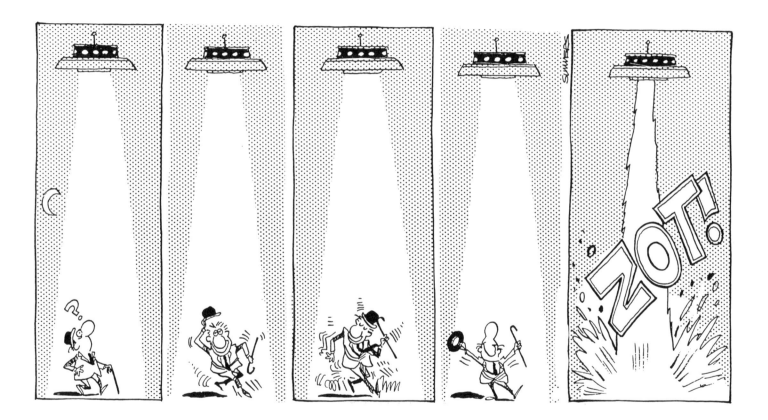